How Good Ol' DR. V Came to Be

Author: Dr. Renée Volny Darko

Illustrated by: Yang Qin

MOUNTAIN ARBOR
PRESS
Alpharetta, GA

ISBN: 978-1-63183-502-5 - Paperback
eISBN: 978-1-63183-503-2 - ePub
eISBN: 978-1-63183-504-9 - mobi

Library of Congress Control Number: 2019937655

Printed in the United States of America   0 3 2 5 1 9

This paper meets the requirements of ANSI/NISO Z39.48-1992 (Permanence of Paper)

Illustrations by Yang Qin

Dedication

This book is dedicated to my maternal grandmother and great-uncle, Claricia and Constantin Volny, and my paternal grandparents, François and Fernande Volny. I am my ancestors' dream because they dared to dream. To my parents, Fred and Marie-Denise Volny, thank you for sacrificing so much of your own dreams so that I could fulfill mine. To my husband, Nii, there is no one with whom I would have rather fulfilled my dream than you. And, finally, to my son, Nii-Amu, who came to me in a dream and who inspired me to write this book, may your dreams never be deferred.

Introduction

This book is not just for kids; it's for the adults in their lives. Read this book to learn how you can support a child's dream of becoming a doctor. Doctors are smart because they enjoy learning, not because they are born perfect or smart. Teach children to enjoy learning, and they'll become smarter and smarter throughout their lives. Learning never ends!

I have a question, a question for you!
How do doctors become what they do?

They listen to my lungs. They listen to my heart.
But, I want to know, how did they start?

So I will ask good ol' Dr. V
how she became what I now see.

She said that since she was a little girl,
becoming a doctor was all she wanted in this world.

She studied and studied very hard in school:
math and science. She wasn't so cool.

But, that was okay, because she would fill
her brain with knowledge with books high as a hill.

She couldn't wait for the day that she'd be
taking care of people who'd call her "Dr. V."

When she grew up, she went to college,
where she would learn and gain more knowledge.

In college, she had a pre-med advisor
to help her along and also to guide her.

She told her advisor that she really liked science,
but she also liked psych, and theater, and finance.

"No worries at all!" her advisor said.
"You can be any major and still be pre-med!"

Psych as her major is the decision she'd make,
but she still had science classes to take.

Biology, chemistry, organic and physics—
these classes were medical-school prerequisites.

She met with her advisor at least four times a year
to make sure that she could overcome her fears.

Four years of college wasn't easy, she'd learn.
Every good grade she got, she worked really hard to earn.

A well-rounded student she soon would become,
involved in campus activities, a leader in some.

In a bit of research she did partake. did
It was not her favorite, so that she'd forsake. leave alone

With lots of hard work, she got her degree,
but she hadn't yet become good ol' Dr. V.

She still had to apply to medical school,
but she also had to follow the rules.

First, she had to take a really big test:
something called the MCAT. Not an animal, I guessed.

The test was tough, so she took it twice.
The second time around, her score was quite nice.

There was another thing she had to do, too:
follow doctors in a hospital to learn what they do.

One of the doctors she worked with before
inspired her so much, he became her mentor.

He wrote her a letter for her application,
and was a great help through this whole situation.

Her pre-med advisor also wrote her a letter,
as did her science professor. She had become a go-getter!

She also wrote an essay all about herself:
why she wanted to be a doctor and not anything else.

Her mentor helped her to make sure it read nice.
Before she was done, she rewrote it twice.

Her med-school application was complete to submit!
On the computer screen, the send button she hit.

The application was sent to many medical schools.
Now she'd wait to hear back, according to the rules.

Each school sent out a secondary application.
She completed them all for schools around the nation.

Interview invitations was the next step, she'd find.
Some schools sent invitations, other schools declined.

She dressed to impress in a dark business suit.
As she remembers it, she looked really cute.

Med-school interviews, she had a total of three.
Would she be accepted? Had to wait and see.

All this waiting was not getting better,
until one day she received a letter.

The day arrived when finally, she'd know
if any schools said yes or if they all said no.

The letter read, "We would like to extend
a position in our school. Will you attend?"

Yes, yes, yes! A thousand times yes!
This day just got better! This day was the best!

Four years later, she finished medical school.
She became a doctor. Now, isn't that cool?

She trained at a hospital to care for kids like me.
And that's how she became good ol' Dr. V!

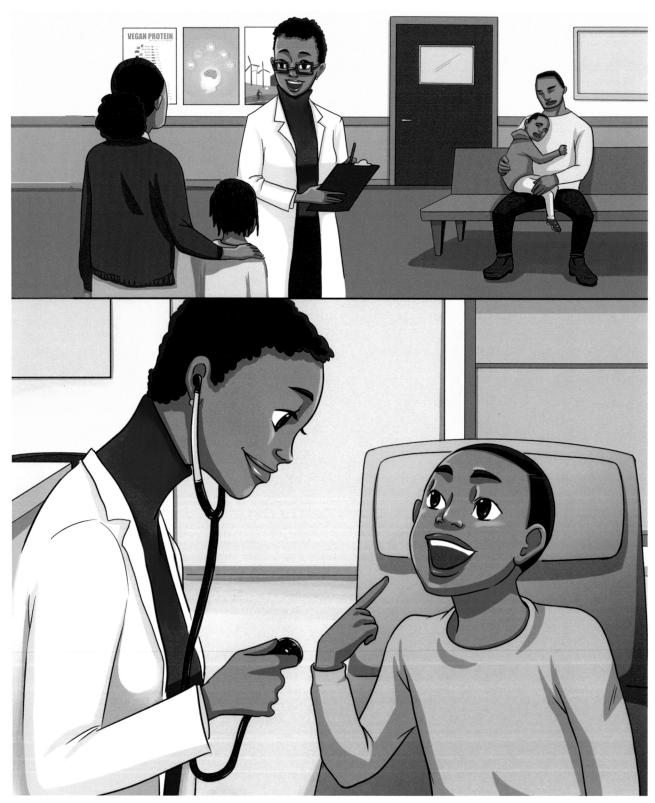

When she ended her story, I asked of her,
"Would you like to be my mentor?"

"Sure!" she said. "I can't wait to see
what a wonderful doctor one day you will be!"

About the Author

When asked by her father what she wanted to be when she grew up, three-year-old Renée said she wanted to be a nurse. When her father asked, "Why not a doctor?", she answered, "Girls can't be doctors!" After her father told her that girls can be doctors, she shifted gears quickly. "Okay! I want to be a doctor!" And so, it began.

But, that was easier said than done. College was more challenging than she thought, but Renée finally graduated. Then, she spent a few more years trying hard and learning even more. She even worked as a tutor and high school science teacher before going to medical school. Renée entered medical school wanting to be a pediatrician, but changed her mind and is now an obstetrician-gynecologist. Dr. Renée delivers babies! She also helps students who want to become doctors, too!

To learn more about Dr. Renée, visit www.DrReneeDarko.com.